HORSES & PONIES STICKER BOOK

Joanna Spector

Edited by Sarah Khan

Designed by Leonard Le Rolland

Illustrated by Sue Testar, David Wright, Elaine Keenan and Malcom McGregor

How to use this book

There are over sixty different horses and ponies in this book. Using the descriptions and pictures, match each sticker with the right animal. If you need help, a list at the back of the book tells you which page each description is on and which sticker goes with it.

You can also use the book as a spotter's handbook to make a note of the horses and ponies you've seen. At the back of the book are explanations of some horse and pony words that you will come across in the descriptions.

Here are some of the words used to describe the parts of a horse:

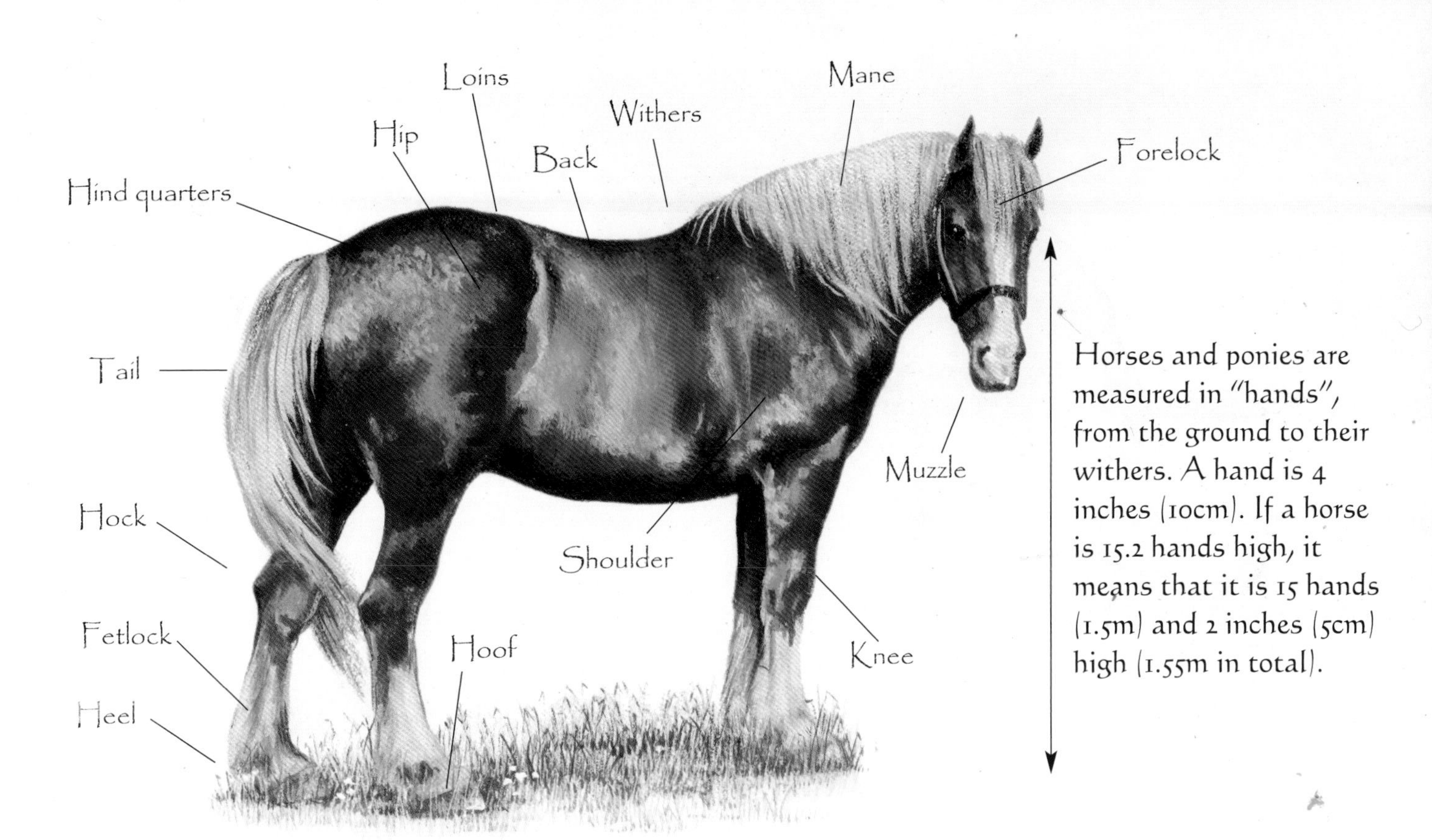

Horses and ponies are measured in "hands", from the ground to their withers. A hand is 4 inches (10cm). If a horse is 15.2 hands high, it means that it is 15 hands (1.5m) and 2 inches (5cm) high (1.55m in total).

Riding horses

Horses are usually more than 14.2 hands high. Different types of horses are used for different kinds of work. Riding horses are fairly light and strong. They are often used for herding cattle, racing, showjumping, dressage and pulling carriages, as well as for riding.

Thoroughbred

Height: 15–16.2 hands

Originally bred from Arab horses in England, Thoroughbreds are the fastest horses in the world. They're elegant and very powerful. They have long legs and their coats can be any solid colour, such as black, grey, bay or chestnut.

WHEN ....

WHERE ....

Arab/Arabian

Height: 14.2–15.1 hands

This horse first came from the deserts of Arabia and is now bred all over the world. It is often used to race long distances. Arabs are usually brown, chestnut, bay, grey or black, with a small, fine head, an arched neck and a short back.

WHEN ....

WHERE ....

Quarter horse

Height: 15–16 hands

Named after the quarter mile races which they used to run, these intelligent American horses are now used on ranches to herd cattle, and for rodeo riding. Their coats can be any colour.

WHEN ....

WHERE ....

American saddlebred

Height: 15–15.3 hands

American saddlebreds are a lively breed that were first used as riding and harness horses in the USA. They have three to five ambling gaits – ways of moving forward with one foot on the ground at a time. This makes them smooth to ride. Their coats are chestnut, brown or bay. See how high they lift their knees and tails as they trot.

WHEN ....

WHERE ....

Morgan

Height: 14–15 hands

These solid American horses were first bred from a stallion called Justin Morgan, in New England. Their coats can be chestnut, brown or bay. Look out for their elegant bodies and thick tails.

WHEN ....

WHERE ....

Riding horses

Tennessee walking horse

Height: 15–16 hands

This horse comes from Tennessee and Louisiana in the USA, and may be any solid colour, or roan. It is used for riding, farm work and pulling carriages. It has three gaits which makes it smooth to ride – a slow walk, running walk and "rocking chair" canter, where the easy rise and fall of the horse's body gently rocks the rider.

WHEN ....

WHERE ....

Paso fino

Height: 13–15.2 hands

Descended from the horses of Spanish explorers, these American show horses have five extra gaits which other horses don't have. Instead of the trot, some have a gait called the "classic fino", where their feet move very quickly but their forward motion is slow.

WHEN ....

WHERE ....

Appaloosa

Height: 14–15.3 hands

This horse was once ridden by the Nez Percé Indians of North America. Its coat can be a dark pinkish shade, with a light back and black spots on the loins and hips. It can also be white with black spots, or bay or black with white spots.

WHEN ....

WHERE ....

Pinto

Height: any height over 14.2 hands

Bred in the USA, pinto horses are used for riding and herding. Their patchy coats can have one of two patterns – "overo", with more white patches on the belly, or "tobiano", with more white patches on the back. Most horses can be bred to have these large white patches.

WHEN ....

WHERE ....

Palomino

Height: any height over 14.2 hands

Palominos have pretty cream coats, with white manes and tails. They are very popular show horses, but are also bred to hunt and jump. Most types of ponies and horses can be bred to have palomino coats.

WHEN ....

WHERE ....

Waler

Height: 15–16 hands

These strong horses were first bred in New South Wales, Australia, and can be any colour. They were once used as cavalry horses, and are now used for riding, showjumping, herding cattle and riding in rodeos.

WHEN ....

WHERE ....

Riding horses

Akhal-teke

Height: about 15.1 hands

This ancient breed comes from Russia, and can bear great heat or cold. They are used for jumping, racing, dressage and trekking. Their fine coats are golden, chestnut, bay, black or brown, with a metallic sheen.

WHEN ....

WHERE ....

Don

Height: 15–16 hands

Once ridden by the Russian Cossack cavalry, these big horses come from the Don Valley in Russia. They have long legs and a short, jerky stride, and are often used to pull carriages. They can be chestnut, beige or grey.

WHEN ....

WHERE ....

Turkoman

Height: 14.3–15.2 hands

This sturdy horse is named after its original home in the Turkoman Steppes in northern Iran. It's a good riding horse because it is so strong and tireless. Its coat is usually grey or bay, but can be dun or chestnut.

WHEN ....

WHERE ....

Barb

Height: 14–15 hands

Barbs are small horses from North Africa, although there are very few pure-bred Barbs left. They have hard legs and feet, and are very fast over short distances. They are usually bay, grey, black, brown or chestnut.

WHEN ....

WHERE ....

Lusitano

Height: 15–16 hands

This pretty Portuguese horse was first bred from Barb and Arab horses and Spanish ponies. It is used by the army and on farms. It's also ridden in bullrings, wearing richly decorated tack (equipment). Its coat is grey, brown or bay.

WHEN ....

WHERE ....

Andalusian

Height: 15.2–16 hands

Popular Spanish riding horses, Andalusians have the same ancestry as the Lusitanos, but are usually shorter and heavier. They are very sure-footed, with grey, black, bay or brown coats. Look out for their arched necks.

WHEN ....

WHERE ....

Riding horses

Hanoverian

Height: 16–17 hands

Descended from war horses ridden in the Middle Ages, this strong German breed has powerful hindquarters and heavy shoulders, and makes a good show-jumper. Its coat is often bay or brown, but can be any solid colour.

WHEN ....

WHERE ....

Holstein

Height: 16–16.2 hands

This big horse comes from the marshes of the River Elbe in Germany. It makes a good show-jumper and carriage horse because it is so strong. Its coat is usually brown, bay or black.

WHEN ....

WHERE ....

Trakehner

Height: 16–16.2 hands

Trakehners are gentle but brave horses bred mainly in Poland and Germany. They're used as farm and cavalry horses, and are also good at jumping and dressage. Their coats can be bay, brown, chestnut or black. Notice how much their shoulders slope.

WHEN ....

WHERE ....

Knabstrup

Height: about 15.2 hands

This attractive Danish horse is descended from a spotted Spanish mare and a Danish stallion. Knabstrups are fast and hardy, and are very popular as circus horses. Their coats are usually white with black spots.

WHEN ....

WHERE ....

Døle/Gudbrandsdal

Height: about 15 hands

Also called Ostlands or Dølehests, these strong horses come from Norway and were once used to pull heavy loads. Their coats are usually brown or bay. Notice their feathered fetlocks.

WHEN ....

WHERE ....

Lipizzaner

Height: 14.3–16 hands

Lipizzaners are Austrian horses used for dressage by the Spanish Riding School in Vienna. They were first bred from Andalusian horses and are born with a black or brown coat, which later turns grey and then white in old age. Notice their short, arched necks.

WHEN ....

WHERE ....

Harness horses

Harness horses are stronger and sturdier than riding horses, and are often good trotters. They make fine driving horses and, in some places, they're also used to pull carts in horse and cart races. Harness horses are also used as working horses on farms, and as riding horses.

Standardbred

Height: 15–16 hands

These are the world's fastest trotting horses. They come from the USA and take part in races pulling two-wheeled carts called sulkies. Standardbreds get their name from the standard speed they needed to reach to be registered for a harness race. Their coats can be any solid colour, but are usually bay, black or brown.

WHEN ....

WHERE ....

Cleveland bay

Height: 15–16.2 hands

Strong and sure-footed, these horses are often used to pull carriages in royal ceremonies in Britain. They're not very fast, but make good jumpers and compete in showjumping competitions. Their coats are bay, with white markings. Notice how much their shoulders slope.

WHEN ....

WHERE ....

Hackney

Height: 15 hands

Hackneys are lively English horses that move gracefully, lifting their legs and tails very high as they trot. They are used as show horses and to pull light carriages. Their coats are bay, black or brown. Look out for their long backs.

WHEN ....

WHERE ....

Frederiksborg

Height: up to 16 hands

These strong and lively horses are an old breed from Denmark. They are hard workers and are often used on farms and as riding horses. They have chestnut coats and fairly short legs.

WHEN ....

WHERE ....

Finnish universal

Height: about 15.2 hands

This gentle and alert horse mainly works on farms and in forests in Finland, but is also used in trotting races and for riding. Its coat is usually chestnut and it often has white markings.

WHEN ....

WHERE ....

Harness horses

Friesian/Frisian

Height: 15–16 hands

This strong, good-natured horse is from Friesland in the Netherlands. It was first bred in the Middle Ages to carry knights, and it now works mostly in harness. It is black, with a thick, curly mane and tail, and feathered fetlocks.

WHEN ....

WHERE ....

Groningen

Height: 15.2–16 hands

Sturdy farm horses from the Netherlands, Groningens can live on very little food. They are heavy but fast, and make very good harness or riding horses. Their coats are usually black, bay or brown.

WHEN ....

WHERE ....

Nonius

Height: 14.2–17 hands

This big, strong horse comes from Hungary, where it was first bred from a stallion called Nonius. It is used mainly as a working horse on farms, and its coat is black, bay or brown. It is bred in two sizes – a small breed of 15.2 hands and a large breed of up to 17 hands.

WHEN ....

WHERE ....

1
2
3
4
5
6

7
8
9
10
11
12

13
14
15
16
17
18

19
20
21
22
14
23
24
25

26
27
28
29
30
31

32
33
34
35
36
37

38
39
40
41
42
43

44
45
46
47
48
49

Orlov trotter

Height: 15.2–17 hands

These strong, heavy horses are named after an 18th century Russian military leader and horse-breeder called Count Orlov. They lift their legs fairly high when trotting, and were once used as cavalry horses. Their coats are often grey, but can be black or bay. Look out for feathering around their fetlocks.

WHEN ....

WHERE ....

Wielkopolski

Height: about 16 hands

A popular Polish horse, Wielkopolskis are bred in many sizes, and are usually chestnut, brown or bay. The heavier ones work on farms, and the lighter ones are used to ride or pull carriages. Many are bred at breeding farms owned by the Polish government.

WHEN ....

WHERE ....

Kladruber

Height: 16–17 hands

Kladrubers are black or grey horses from the Czech and Slovak republics and were first bred in the 16th century by Emperor Maximilian II. They are used to pull coaches at official ceremonies, and are also seen on farms and in dressage competitions.

WHEN ....

WHERE ....

Heavy horses

Heavy horses are the largest breeds of horses. They are much bigger and chunkier than riding horses and harness horses, and are also very strong. They are mainly used to work on farms and to haul heavy loads. In the Middle Ages, many of them were used to carry knights into battle.

Shire

Height: 17–over 18 hands

These English heavy horses were once ridden by medieval knights. They're hard workers, and are now used as working horses on farms. Their coats are usually grey, bay or black, with white markings. Look out for their feathered fetlocks.

WHEN ....

WHERE ....

Suffolk punch

Height: about 16 hands

Named after their original home in Suffolk, England, this rare, stocky breed tend to be very good-natured and can live on very little food. Their coats are always chestnut. Notice their thick necks and wide chests.

WHEN ....

WHERE ....

Percheron

Height: 15.2–17 hands

This popular working horse first came from northern France. It is very strong and often weighs over a tonne, but it only needs a little food. It is also very quiet and easy to handle. Its silky coat can be black or grey.

WHEN ....

WHERE ....

Breton heavy

Height: 15–16 hands

These strong and rugged horses from northwest France are mainly used as working horses. They are usually roan, but can also be bay or chestnut.

WHEN ....

WHERE ....

Ardennes/Ardennais

Height: about 15.2 hands

An ancient breed from France and Belgium, these horses were once used by the cavalry of the French emperor, Napoleon. They are strong and gentle, and can live out in bad weather. Their coats are usually chestnut, roan or bay. Notice their heavy necks and shoulders.

WHEN ....

WHERE ....

Heavy horses

Pinzgauer noriker

Height: 15–16 hands

This strong, quiet horse is the oldest breed in Austria, and may have been descended from a Roman breed. It is often used as a working horse on farms. Its coat is bay, chestnut or spotted.

WHEN ....

WHERE ....

Schleswig

Height: 15.2–16 hands

Schleswigs are strong, powerful horses from northern Germany. They once carried knights into battle, but are now used mostly on farms and for hauling work. Their coats are usually chestnut.

WHEN ....

WHERE ....

Dutch heavy

Height: 16.3 hands

Bred from Belgian horses, this strong, ancient breed is very popular as a working horse on farms in the Netherlands. Their coats are bay, chestnut or grey.

WHEN ....

WHERE ....

Jutland

Height: 15.2–15.3 hands

These strong Danish horses have large bodies and short legs. They were once ridden by the Vikings, but now work on farms and pull brewers' wagons in Denmark. Their coats are often chestnut, but can be roan, black, grey, bay or light brown.

WHEN ....

WHERE ....

Vladimir

Height: about 16 hands

Named after their original home in Vladimir, Russia, these strong, active horses are often used for harness work. Their coats can be bay, chestnut or roan. Look out for their high, arched necks.

WHEN ....

WHERE ....

Ponies

Ponies are smaller than horses, at a height of 14.2 hands, or under. A few ponies still live wild in herds, on moors and in forests or hilly places, but most of them have been tamed, and are now kept as riding ponies or pets.

Exmoor

Height: up to 12.3 hands

These strong, powerful ponies are the oldest breed in Britain, and most still live half wild in herds on the heaths and moors of Exmoor. They are always brown or bay, with a light belly and nose. Tame Exmoor ponies are very popular riding ponies for children.

WHEN ....

WHERE ....

Dartmoor

Height: up to 12.2 hands

Most of these tough little British ponies roam half wild on the hills and moors of Dartmoor. They have small, pretty heads, and their coats may be bay, black or brown. Dartmoor ponies are intelligent and can make a good children's riding pony.

WHEN ....

WHERE ....

Fell

Height: about 14 hands

Fell ponies are large and sturdy, and come from the Pennine hills in Britain. They're still used by farmers for herding sheep and cattle. Usually black, Fell ponies can also be brown or bay, but never have any white markings.

WHEN ....

WHERE ....

Highland

Height: up to 14.2 hands

Good at travelling long distances, this large pony comes from the highlands of Scotland. It's usually grey or dun, but can also be black or chestnut. Look out for its thick mane and tail, and its long coat in winter.

WHEN ....

WHERE ....

Shetland

Height: about 9.2 hands

This strong little pony comes from the Shetland Islands in Britain and is a popular pet. Its rough coat is usually brown, black or chestnut, but can also be piebald or skewbald. Notice its short neck.

WHEN ....

WHERE ....

Ponies

Welsh mountain

Height: up to 12 hands

Welsh mountain ponies are an old breed from Wales, descended from Arab and Thoroughbred horses. Popular for riding and driving, they have elegant heads and their coats can be any colour, except piebald or skewbald.

WHEN ....

WHERE ....

Camargue

Height: up to 14.2 hands

From swampland at the mouth of the River Rhône in France, this ancient breed is very strong and tough. Some ponies are used to herd cattle, but many of them still live wild in herds.

WHEN ....

WHERE ....

Connemara

Height: 13–14.2 hands

This attractive pony comes from northwest Ireland, and was probably first bred from Spanish and Arab horses. It is fast and sure-footed, and its coat is usually grey, but can also be dun, black, brown, bay or chestnut.

WHEN ....

WHERE ....

Gotland/Russ

Height: about 12.2 hands

This ancient breed has lived on the Swedish island of Gotland since the Stone Age. They are very good trotters and jumpers, and their coats can be any colour, but are usually brown, bay or chestnut.

WHEN ....

WHERE ....

Haflinger

Height: about 14 hands

Pretty and sure-footed, these Austrian ponies are used in forestry work and to pull and carry loads up hills. They're also ridden and driven in harness. Look out for their chestnut coats and flaxen manes and tails.

WHEN ....

WHERE ....

Fjord

Height: 13–14.2 hands

This strong Norwegian pony is used for all types of work, such as riding, driving, hauling and carrying. Look out for its yellow dun coat, and its black and silver mane which is usually trimmed by its owner into the shape of a crest.

WHEN ....

WHERE ....

Ponies

Caspian

Height: 9.2–11.2 hands

Caspian ponies are a small, dainty breed from Iran. Their long legs make them look like tiny Thoroughbred horses and make them very good at jumping. Their coats are usually bay, brown or grey and never have any white markings.

WHEN ....

WHERE ....

Przewalski

Height: 12–14 hands

Also called the Asiatic or Mongolian wild horse, this tough breed hasn't changed since the Ice Age. Only a few exist, and they are mostly kept in zoos. They are bay or dun, with a big head and stubby mane.

WHEN ....

WHERE ....

Sable Island pony

Height: about 14 hands

This small pony comes from Nova Scotia in Canada. Its coat is usually chestnut, but can be any shade. It still lives in wild herds and feeds off scrub grass on sand dunes. Tame ones are used as children's riding ponies.

WHEN ....

WHERE ....

Criollo

Height: 14 hands and over

Descended from Spanish horses such as Barbs and Andalusians, these big ponies come from South America. They are good jumpers and are used to play polo. Their coats are dun, roan, brown, skewbald, black or bay.

WHEN ....

WHERE ....

Falabella

Height: less than 7 hands

These tiny little ponies come from Argentina. They're not very strong, but are good-natured and make popular pets and driving ponies. They have long, silky coats, which can be any colour.

WHEN ....

WHERE ....

Pony of the Americas (POA)

Height: 11.2–13.2 hands

This pony is a modern breed from the USA, and makes a good children's riding pony. Its coat has a spotted pattern, which is similar to the coat of Appaloosa horses. Look out for its dark muzzle.

WHEN ....

WHERE ....

Index and checklist

This list will help you to find every horse and pony in the book. The first number after each animal's name tells you which page it's on. The second number (in brackets) is the number of its sticker.

Horse and pony words

bay	a light to dark brown horse with black lower legs, mane and tail
cavalry	soldiers on horseback
chestnut	reddish-brown
dressage	a method of training horses, often displayed at competitions
driving horse	a horse used to pull carts or carriages
dun	a pale beige horse, with black legs and a dark stripe along its back
flaxen	pale yellow
gaits	a horse's different paces
hand	unit for measuring a horse's height from hoof to withers, equal to 4in (10cm)
pack pony	a pony used to carry loads
piebald	a black horse with white patches
polo	a game played on horseback
pure-bred	descended from one breed of horse
roan	a bay, black or chestnut horse, with a sprinkling of white hairs on its coat
rodeo	an American horse show at which cowboys display riding and herding skills
skewbald	a horse of any colour, except black, with white patches
stallion	a male horse used for breeding
trekking	long-distance riding

Front cover © Rex Stucky/NATIONAL GEOGRAPHIC IMAGE COLLECTION/ Getty Images
Back cover © Lothar Lenz/zefa/Corbis (Back cover)
Cover design: Michael Hill
Digital imaging: Will Dawes and Keith Furnival

This edition first published in 2006 by Usborne Publishing Ltd., 83-85 Saffron Hill, London EC1N 8RT, England.

Printed in Malaysia.